Published in association with
Yates & Yates // www.yates2.com.

Book art design, illustrations, and cover design by
Jenn Jett // www.jennjett.com

ISBN: 978-0-692-97567-1

First Edition: January 2018

Look Inside

CAMBRIA JOY

with love & joy,

Cambria Joy

forward

I have written this devotional because I have felt your pain in my heart. I know what it's like to be in a constant battle with the mirror. I remember the prayer that I prayed to God years ago all too well. I had just binged. Again. My battle with the mirror waged on. I prayed, "God, if I ever get out, if You deliver me out of this fight, I'm going to help her. I'm going to help her get out and find her way out too."

Who is "her"?

She's you.

Maybe you're in bondage to the mirror too? You feel that if you don't perfect your image you'll never be happy. Maybe you've held tightly to this wish for so long that is has become your greatest hope. I will say, my friend, that there is a greater hope, a living hope, that is not found in the mirror. We've fixed our eyes so long on the outward that we *think* real beauty is found there. 1 Samuel 16:7 says, "But the Lord said to Samuel, "Do not look at his appearance or at his physical stature, because I have refused him. For the *Lord does* not *see* as man sees; for man looks at the outward appearance, but the Lord looks at the heart." Jesus is calling us to turn our eyes away from ourselves and back to Him. We were created to reflect His image not to perfect our own. When we fix our eyes on Him rather than our reflection we are transformed by His truth so that we can rest in who He says we are - not in who the mirror says we are.

God created women with a unique desire for community and closeness. We depend on and look to one another for answers to questions that we all face. Yet, sometimes we find ourselves a little lost in a spot without anyone to ask for help and the feelings of loneliness settle in. We begin to wonder where to go next and if we will ever find our way back on the right path.

My prayer for you for the next 30 days is that you begin your journey home. The Bible says in Ephesians 3:17, "that Christ may dwell in your hearts through faith; that you, being rooted and grounded in love." That is my ultimate prayer for you this month, that as you trust Jesus Christ with all of your heart He will make His home there.

I invite you to read each day and see if my journey might provide you answers, guidance, and ultimately give you hope on yours. I don't have all the answers but I know who does. His name is Jesus Christ and He is the answer.

I hope that you can sit down every day for a little while, get away from the distractions of life, pour yourself a hot cup of tea, and read each day as if it was written for you alone. May you be strengthened on your journey as you turn your eyes away from the mirror and begin to look inside to see yourself as your heavenly Father sees you. Let's do this, together.

With love,
Cambria Joy

TABLE OF CONTENTS

grace

...MY GRACE IS
SUFFICIENT FOR YOU,
FOR MY STRENGTH IS
MADE PERFECT
IN WEAKNESS...

2 CORINTHIANS 12:9

When our strength runs out,
Jesus's grace will not.

I will never forget that night. I sat at the edge of my bed with my head bowed low. My heart was broken, and I could not cry one more tear. I'd never felt more defeated. Earlier that night I'd worked out at the gym to the point of near exhaustion only to fall back into the pit of overeating - again. I came home and downed one whole pint of ice cream, 3 bowls of cereal, and almost an entire loaf of bread. I felt sick because of how full I was, but I felt empty inside my soul.

Just hours before I'd felt strong and powerful - my endorphins were high, and I felt the pride of being disciplined and having self-control. But now I felt weak to the point that I could barely lift my head - maybe the weakest I'd ever been. Putting my hope in my own strength had left me worn out.

Paul the apostle wrote about the "thorn" in his flesh. The Bible doesn't say what that thorn was, but perhaps it was a physical illness or weakness of some kind. Paul pleaded with God to take it away. The Lord responded, "My grace is sufficient for you, for My strength is made perfect in weakness," (2 Corinthians 12:9). As someone who's tried desperately to be strong and in total control, this verse resonates deeply with me.

What a gift it is to know that in moments of weakness, we are more qualified than ever to step into His grace and experience the strength of God. "For when I am weak, then I am strong," 2 Corinthians 12:10 says. This is good news! Even at our weakest we are strong because of Him!

Well that night as I sat on my bed, God heard my tears. In the darkness of the night, a light turned on in my heart. I realized my strength is not found in my own power and endurance. He, Himself is my strength.

2 Corinthians 9:8 says, "And God *is* able to make all grace abound toward you, that you, always having all sufficiency in all *things*, may have an abundance for every good work." I felt that grace that night and I learned something vitally important: When our strength runs out, Jesus's grace will not. When you can't take another step, grace will carry you. And when you feel like giving up, remember that in your lowest moments His love won't give up on you. Nothing can separate you from the love of God that is ours through Jesus. Not even your weakest moments can bring you low enough to lose His power.

reflection

What happens when you rely on your own strength rather than God-sized strength when facing mountains in your life?

Even in your weakest moment, you are still God-strong. God will strengthen your heart. Psalm 73:26 "My flesh and my heart fail; *But* God *is* the strength of my heart and my portion forever."

Ask God to help you to run with the perseverance that comes from His strength and not your own. Hebrews 12:1 "Therefore we also, since we are surrounded by so great a cloud of witnesses, let us lay aside every weight, and the sin which so easily ensnares *us*, and let us run with endurance the race that is set before us."

identity

GOD CREATED
MAN IN HIS
OWN IMAGE

GENESIS 1:27

You are created by God, not to perfect your own image, but to reflect His image.

I used to weigh myself every day. When the number was lower I would smile to myself in my victory! On days the number was higher I felt defeated. But no matter what the scale said, I was never really at peace with my body. Regardless of my weight I would look into the mirror and feel the need to make a change.

My feelings led to dangerous actions. Skipping meals, excessive workouts, and restriction became normal to me. I repeated the inspiring verse, "I can do all things through Christ!" and then I'd foolishly pop a diet pill.

My image had begun to rule me. Slowly I began to serve the mirror. My thoughts revolved around my looks. Every bite of food, or lack thereof, was about perfecting the image. An idol was forming in my mind and heart - an obsession with my appearance.

One day I read this verse from Genesis 1:27 and saw it in a new light, "So God created man in His *own* image; in the image of God He created him; male and female He created them." The profound simplicity of this verse enlightened a part of my heart that had been in the dark for years. I was made in the image of God. As simple as that truth is, it sunk deep into my heart and began a transforming work.

When I look in the mirror I am seeing my physical image. I believed that image needed to be changed and perfected before I could accept myself. Yet, when I look at Jesus I am invited to see myself as He sees me - accepted in the Beloved (Ephesians 1:6).

You have the fingerprint of God on you. Because you are made in His image according to His likeness you can look in the mirror and say, "I am handmade by God and my joy is found in my identity in Christ."

We will always be tempted to never be satisfied with how we look. We will run and strive and still never reach the finish line. With Jesus you start at the finish line. God's Word says you are beautifully and wonderfully made in Psalm 139:14. When He hung on the cross He declared, "It is finished!" meaning Jesus' finished work on the cross makes you clothed with the righteousness of God through Christ Jesus.

Your worth cannot be measured on a scale and you are more than just an image reflected in a mirror. You are created by God, not to perfect your own image, but to reflect His image.

reflection

When you look in the mirror, remember who you are in Him. "...'Fear not, for I have redeemed you; I have called *you* by your name; You *are* Mine.' " (Isaiah 43:1).

Ask God to help you reflect Jesus instead of focusing on your physical appearance, which will not come with you into eternity. "All flesh *is* as grass, And all the glory of man as the flower of the grass. The grass withers, And its flower falls away, But the word of the Lord endures forever." (1 Peter 1:24-25).

When you go for your workout today, remind yourself you are doing this to respect the body that God has given you. Tell yourself, "I accept my body right now and I'm doing this workout for the glory of God."

sunset

BUT THOSE WHO
WAIT ON THE
LORD SHALL
RENEW THEIR
STRENGTH...

ISAIAH 40:31

With Jesus you start at the finish line.

I love to go for sunset runs. Everyone seems to gather at the edge of the Earth to watch the sun sink into the horizon and I love being one of the on-lookers. As the sky wishes today farewell, everything around me looks golden with colors painted by heaven. Maybe that's why I love it so much, because there's something heavenly about those runs; an earthly reminder of God's faithfulness day after day. Sunset after sunset.

I love to meditate on scripture during runs like, Isaiah 40:31. "But those who wait on the Lord Shall renew *their* strength; They shall mount up with wings like eagles, They shall run and not be weary, They shall walk and not faint."

When it comes to physical fitness I'm impatient and want to reach my goals as quickly as possible. But I have found that I burn out too easily, get tired too quickly, and give up too early. That's where Jesus comes in. Isaiah 40:28 says, "Have you not known? Have you not heard? The everlasting God, the Lord, The Creator of the ends of the earth, Neither faints nor is weary. His understanding is unsearchable."

It's easy to quickly become weary on your fitness journey. The Creator of the universe is the same Creator of you and He never grows weary. When you're tempted to give up because you're not seeing progress, it's too hard, or you feel like you've messed up again, remember the faithful grace of God. It's available for you day after day, sunset after sunset. Don't be afraid of messing up or falling. Remember with Jesus you start at the finish line. Press into Him when you feel as if you can't press on.

Jesus is patient with you so be patient with yourself. When we learn to walk patiently with Jesus, we can run with Him with endurance. Wait on Him and He will renew your strength. And you will learn that you will not only run but you will soar.

reflection

Memorize Isaiah 40:31. Hide this truth in your heart for the days you feel weary.

Ask the Lord to help you see the beauty in creation as you enjoy working out.

Are you having a hard time being patient in this season? As you wait on God ask Him to renew your strength and give you joy. Romans 12:12 says to be, "rejoicing in hope, patient in tribulation, continuing steadfastly in prayer."

...BRINGING
EVERY THOUGHT
INTO CAPTIVITY
TO THE OBEDIENCE
OF CHRIST

2 CORINTHIANS 10:5

That's what happened when I
believed the lie of
"skinny = happiness."
I was on the road to destruction.

I used to believe that being thinner would make me happier. That being thinner would make people like me more. That being thinner would make me like me more.

In fact, I believed that lie for such a long time that being thinner became my dearest hope in my deceived heart.

This false hope consumed me and I took my mind off of Jesus. James 1:14 says, "But each one is tempted when he is drawn away by his own desires and enticed." I desired more than anything to be skinny. My heart's treasure was to attain skinny, but that's fools gold. False treasure may look pretty but ultimately it holds no value or worth. It's just pretty to look at. That's why we need to be careful when we place our desires above God's truth. Don't let the desires of your heart deceive you into settling for fools gold.

When we try to do things our way, we can be so willful, can't we? We try to fill ourselves with what we think is good, but the Bible is clear in Proverbs 14:12 that, "There is a way *that seems* right to a man, But its end *is* the way of death."

That's what happened when I believed the lie of "skinny = happiness." I was on the road to destruction. I walked that road for a long time and never arrived at happiness.

So how do we protect our minds from falling victim to lies and chasing after our own desires? Romans 13:14 says to, "But put on the Lord Jesus Christ, and make no provision for the flesh, to *fulfill its* lusts." Choose today to believe His Truth instead. Confess to Him the things you have chased in His place, and decide you will no longer feed any desire that wants to be first in your heart.

reflection

Are you believing lies about yourself? See 2 Corinthians 10:5. Ask God to help you take every thought captive to Christ to discern what is good.

Here are truths to let sink deep into your heart: There is no condemnation in Christ. You are more loved than you could ever comprehend. You are forgiven of your deepest sin. Nothing can ever separate you from the love of God.

Grab a sticky note and write something encouraging on it whether it be a Bible verse or something like, "I am hand crafted by the God who made the universe," and place it on your mirror. The note will speak life every time you look at it. Refuse to feed thoughts that try to pull you away from truth.

TRUST IN THE LORD
WITH ALL YOUR
HEART, AND LEAN
NOT ON YOUR OWN
UNDERSTANDING

PROVERBS 3:5

When you feel tempted to
become upset with what you're
seeing in the mirror,
remember that God who began
a good work in you will carry it
out until the day of completion.

I know what it's like to work out, eat healthy, and care for your body, only to look in the mirror and not see any changes. Have you felt this way before? I love that God's word has something to say about this. Who you are eternally in Christ far outweighs who you are temporally in the mirror.

I also understand the struggle of knowing the truth but wrestling to believe in it. The goal is to care for our bodies as an amazing gift from God. To glorify Him without becoming self-absorbed, because we know that God doesn't look at the outward appearance but at the heart. Yet discouragement can be quick to knock on the door when you feel as if your hard work is not working.

The Bible says that we walk by faith and not by sight in 2 Corinthians 5:7. When you feel tempted to become upset with what you're seeing in the mirror, remember that God who began a good work in you will carry it out until the day of completion (Philippians 1:6). God wants to do a good work on your heart. When we keep our eyes on Jesus as we sweat in the gym, our heart is changed first and then the physical changes follow. It's no longer about serving the mirror but rather thanking God for the body and breath He has graciously given us. The external changes become secondary to the internal changes. Be encouraged that God knows exactly how you're feeling. He sees your tears and hears your cries. You are fully known in your weakness by Him and at the very same time fully equipped with strength from Him.

Learning to walk by faith is challenging when you cannot see. Yet just because you can't see doesn't mean you should give up. In fact now is the time to press on more than ever before, remember Romans 5:3-4, "And not only *that*, but we also glory in tribulations, knowing that tribulation produces perseverance; and perseverance, character; and character, hope."

God is producing in us an everlasting reward that is of infinite worth. The mirror produces in us a temporal reward that is of finite worth. He wants you to desire Him above all else, so that when you taste the sweet changes on the inside you will realize that the outside changes are nowhere near as satisfying. "Oh, taste and see that the Lord is good; Blessed *is* the man *who* trusts in Him!" (Psalm 34:8). I have learned that the physical changes in my body, though good, are nothing compared to the eternal changes in my heart.

When you're not seeing the changes in your body you want to see, have faith, and look a little deeper. Rest assured God is doing amazing work to change you from the inside out.

reflection

It's easy to take your eyes off of Jesus and walk by sight. Ask God to help you to "Trust in the Lord with all your heart, And lean not on your own understanding," Proverbs 3:5.

When you start to allow the mirror to dictate your feelings, remind yourself that your joy comes from the Lord. Read Psalm 28:7.

Your hard work in the gym is not in vain when you are taking care of the body God has given you. Give yourself permission to abide in God's timeline and not your own.

...FORGETTING THOSE THINGS WHICH ARE BEHIND AND REACHING FORWARD TO THOSE THINGS WHICH ARE AHEAD

PHILIPPIANS 3:13

Our progress is not marked by
perfection but by grace.

CHAPTER SIX // PROGRESS > PERFECTION

I love that the Lord's mercies are new every morning. Every day is a chance to let go of yesterday's mistakes and walk in the newness of today.

I have spent too many mornings moping around because I overate the evening before. On those days, I felt like a failure, and I struggled to put on my gym clothes and get moving because yesterday's failure was stuck in my head!

Moving forward requires looking forward. And it's awfully difficult to move forward while looking back. Don't allow your past to hinder your progress. Don't let yesterday steal today.

It's easy to look into the rear view mirror and feel defeated. Why not change your perspective? If you're going to look back take a quick glance, remind yourself how far you have come, and then keep marching ahead. Perfection will lie about the future based on mistakes made in the past. Don't listen to perfection. Who holds the future? Oh yeah, Jesus does. So listen to Him. Remember what Paul said in Philippians 3:13, "...one thing *I do*, forgetting those things which are behind and reaching forward to those things which are ahead."

What a beautiful and bold example we have in Jesus Christ who reached forward to the hardest thing of all. The cross. Jesus knew the road to His death would not be easy. What a great hope we have in Him, "who for the joy set before Him endured the cross," Hebrews 12:2. He pressed on knowing that the difficulty ahead was nothing compared to crossing the finish line.

May we have the mind of Christ in knowing that our progress is not marked by perfection but by grace. And the grace that allows you to forgive your past is the grace that holds your hand moving into the future.

reflection

Thank God specifically for the progress that He's helped you with this far and ask Him to help you to keep your eyes on Him as you move forward.

Do you find yourself getting caught up too often in the past? Hide Philippians 3:12 in your heart.

During your next workout, confess and let go of perfectionism and commit to stay focused on progressing from one moment to the next. Focusing on the present gives us energy for this moment!

FOR BODILY EXERCISE
PROFITS A LITTLE,
BUT GODLINESS
IS PROFITABLE
FOR ALL THINGS...

I TIMOTHY 4:8

When I put my love for fitness
above my love for Jesus life
gets pretty messy.

1 Timothy 4:8 "For bodily exercise profits a little, but godliness is profitable for all things, having promise of the life that now is and of that which is to come."

I'm so glad God put this verse in the Bible. He directly says that bodily exercise gives us a profit. Now I don't know about you but that makes me pretty happy. I like to work out and I want to be strong, and God says right here in His word that it profits us! He then goes onto say that godliness is profitable for all things.

Scripture often hits us right where we're prideful, doesn't it? God's Word says that exercise is good. But there is something far better. Godly living produces a far greater reward than physical training. Why? Because we can't take our earthly bodies to heaven. Our heavenly Father is far more concerned with our spiritual strength than our physical strength.

Taking care of your body, which is the temple of the Holy Spirit, is honoring to God. But failing to take care of your spirit is neglecting to care for what God considers to be of greater importance. I believe this verse is here to balance our loves. We should love disciplining ourselves to be obedient to Christ more than disciplining our bodies in the gym.

I can tell you from personal experience that when I put my love for fitness above my love for Jesus life gets pretty messy. Working out is a beautiful thing when our first love is Jesus because it allows us to serve our Lord rather than serve ourselves. When things are reversed, our bodies can become our idols and we can become earthly minded instead of heavenly minded.

God wants us to have no other idols before Him. The greatest devotion and affection you should have is for Jesus. Endeavor to be healthy for the glory of God rather than for the glory of yourself!

reflection

Do you find that spending time with God in the morning conflicts with your workouts?

Ask God to help you understand what 1 Timothy 4:8 looks like in your own life. What does it look like to strengthen your body and your spirit in the same day? Ask Him to help you to make a routine of sticking to your workouts while also committing to spending time with Him.

Try taking breaks during your workouts and reading scripture while you're catching your breath. I used to love doing this when I ran a lot. I had a favorite bench that I would sit at that marked the halfway point during my run. I would take that time to read God's Word, stretch a little, and mentally prepare to finish the rest of my run.

THEREFORE WHOEVER
HEARS THESE SAYINGS
OF MINE, AND DOES
THEM, I WILL LIKEN HIM
TO A WISE MAN WHO
BUILT HIS HOUSE ON
THE ROCK

MATTHEW 7:24

Instead of working out and eating to be thin, work out to simply honor the body that God gave you.

CHAPTER EIGHT // BUILD ON THE ROCK

When I first started working out, my goal was simple: I wanted to be thin. I didn't care about honoring God with my body. I cared about what my body looked like.

My prideful heart had no intention of honoring God with my actions. I just wanted to be fit for selfish reasons. I was doing it for myself! Isn't that what all of the Pinterest quotes say to do it for? "Do it for you!"

The Bible is clear in Proverbs 16:18 that, "Pride *goes* before destruction, And a haughty spirit before a fall." I can tell you that my pride had laid the foundation and destruction came soon after. Working out for my selfish, prideful reason of looking good quickly fell through. I became discouraged when I didn't see change right away, and when I couldn't make it to the gym I felt like I had failed to move a little closer in perfecting my image for the day.

When I read Matthew 7:24, I recognized myself. I learned that before I build the house, (taking care of my body), I need to lay the right foundation. A foundation that wanted to honor my God-given body was the strong foundation I needed in order to build a safe house. Instead of working out and eating to be thin, I now work out to simply honor the body that God gave me.

Founded in Christ, my desire to work out actually increased because I wasn't focused on my own performance. I just kept my eyes on Jesus and when the rains came (the discouragement) my house did not fall. In fact because I had weathered the storm, I found that my confidence in Christ increased. He is your rock. Instead of building your plans on the sand, let them be found in Christ and He will never let you down.

reflection

Do you feel as if you have had the wrong motives in your workouts? It's easy to fix our eyes on the wrong thing when it comes to fitness. Ask God to help you to workout with the intentions that He wants you to have.

Read Matthew 7:24-27 and ask God to help you build your house on solid ground. "Therefore whoever hears these sayings of Mine, and does them, I will liken him to a wise man who built his house on the rock: and the rain descended, the floods came, and the winds blew and beat on that house; and it did not fall, for it was founded on the rock. But everyone who hears these sayings of Mine, and does not do them, will be like a foolish man who built his house on the sand: and the rain descended, the floods came, and the winds blew and beat on that house; and it fell. And great was its fall."

Grab your favorite pen and a journal. Write down your new intentions of working out such as, "I will workout because I am thankful for my beating heart and both of my legs. I will workout to thank God for the gift that my body is."

AND HE SAID
TO THEM,
'COME ASIDE
BY YOURSELVES
TO A DESERTED
PLACE AND
REST A WHILE...'

MARK 6:31

Our dependence on Christ is going to carry us farther than our dependence on ourselves.

You were created to rest. How often do we forget that in our busy lives? Rest can look a little different each day. Sometimes it means skipping your evening workout class to just watch a movie with your family. Sometimes it means having a date with yourself and the beach to simply stop and listen to the waves. It's interesting to note that rest was created before the fall of man. Therefore it was not made by God in order to give us a "break" in this sinful world. It was good in and of itself, before sin even entered. So that leads me to believe that if God rested on the seventh day and He created rest before sin came in, we ought to be like Him, and rest ourselves.

On your fitness journey, remember that rest is just as important, if not more important, than working. When you work out you are tearing down your muscles during exercise in order to make them stronger. In order for them to rebuild properly you need to rest. You must rest in order to rebuild. In the craziness of life, it is much easier to keep going than to actively pause. But Jesus begins in John 15:5, "I am the vine, you *are* the branches. He who abides in Me, and I in him, bears much fruit..." Only when we are actively abiding in Him will we produce fruit. In our own efforts and striving, we are fruitless.

The mistake I have made, and can still make, is thinking that I can do everything, including taking care of my body, on my own. Jesus finishes in John 15:5 by saying, "for without Me, you can do nothing," I don't know about you but that leaves me feeling pretty inadequate in my own strength! Never fear, here comes the classic Philippians 4:13, "I can do all things through Christ who strengthens me."

All of these verses have something in common: our dependence on Christ is going to carry us farther than our dependence on ourselves. All too often we fall short of God's promises by striving instead of abiding. There is so much more of God's gifts to be enjoyed when we press in by faith and take what God desires for us, simply by giving up the striving and learning to abide.

reflection

What area of your life do you need to learn to abide instead of strive?

Read Hebrews 4:9-10. "There remains therefore a rest for the people of God. For he who has entered His rest has himself also ceased from his works as God *did* from His." Ask God to grant you wisdom to know when to actively pause.

The next time you decide to skip a workout because you're tired remind yourself that it's more than ok! God has given us an amazing internal ability to know when our bodies are fatigued and it's time to take a break. Thank you Jesus for the gift of rest that is ours not only for today, but for eternity.

don't

THEREFORE DO NOT
WORRY ABOUT
TOMORROW, FOR
TOMORROW WILL
WORRY ABOUT
ITS OWN THINGS...

MATTHEW 6:34

All we need is faith for today.

CHAPTER TEN // DON'T WORRY ABOUT A THING

Matthew 6:34 "Therefore do not worry about tomorrow, for tomorrow will worry about its own things. Sufficient for the day is its own trouble."

If you're like me, you worry about tomorrow. The future's uncertain, and uncertainty can breed fear if not carefully placed in God's hands. I like that Jesus is very real with us. He literally says, "sufficient for the day *is* its own trouble." There is no sugar coating in the Bible. Today has enough trouble, and Jesus acknowledges that.

A life of faith means we get to live fully in the moment. Fear of the future no longer has a hold on us. Sometimes that fear may creep in, but Jesus frees us from it - if we let Him.

I remember a specific time when I was fearful about the future. In high school I struggled with binge eating disorder and I can tell you I definitely did not "laugh without fear of the future" like the Proverbs 31 woman. I was terrified I might never be free of my eating disorder. I worried constantly about tomorrow, wondering if I might fall back into old obsessions and patterns while at the same time being scared to let go of control.

But God is not confined to time. In fact He stands outside of time, which means He is in just as much of tomorrow as He is in today. He is with you now. And just because you haven't made it to tomorrow doesn't change that He is already there.

I was worried that I would always be in a downward spiral with my eating disorder and that I would never be able to eat normal again. Everyday was getting worse, and worse, and worse. God reminded me to trust Him *today*, one day at a time. That's all I needed to do. When I released my worries about *today*, He changed my heart about tomorrow.

All we need is faith for today. Do not let the enemy of tomorrow enter in the door of today. God will bring you through today's troubles, and He guarantees He will be with you tomorrow as well.

reflection

Have you ever found yourself fearful of tomorrow because of today's circumstances? Check out what Corrie Ten Boom said about that, "Worry does not empty tomorrow of its sorrow. It empties today of its strength."

Read Matthew 6:34, and ask God to help you to not worry about tomorrow. Ask Him instead to give you just enough strength for today.

When fear about the future starts to creep in, thank God for the blessings in your life. Use gratitude to refocus on God's blessings and provision. Remind yourself that every day is a gift, even the very breath in your lungs is something to rejoice in.

He wi

THE LORD WILL
FIGHT FOR YOU,
AND YOU SHALL
HOLD YOUR PEACE

EXODUS 14:14

"The Lord will fight for you,
and you shall hold your peace."
Exodus 14:14

CHAPTER ELEVEN // HE WILL FIGHT YOUR BATTLES

Exodus 14:14 "The Lord will fight for you, and you shall hold your peace."

I was sixteen. With tear-filled eyes I looked hopefully into the eyes of my youth leader. I shared with her how I felt like I was going in circles fighting this eating disorder, swinging at something I could never hit. It wasn't just a battle - it was an all-out war, 24/7.

She looked at me and said these soothing words, "The Lord will fight for you, Cambria. He will fight your battles." Like aloe vera on a sunburn, her words spoke relief to my heart and immediately began their healing work. She spoke the words of Exodus 14:14 and I felt the truth of God's Word quite literally soothing my soul.

You see the battle I was fighting was not my eating disorder, it was my un-surrendered heart. I needed to give over my future to God and trust that He would not only fight for me, but deliver me. I knew that God was with me and that He was helping me, but what I didn't realize is that God didn't want to just be my right hand man in battle, He wanted to be my Savior. It was not my job to fight this battle, it was my job to let God do *His* job.

That night I gave up position as captain and let Jesus step into that rightful role. I found that He lead me a lot better than I lead me. When we give Jesus the right place in our life, He will do immeasurably more than all we can ask or think of Him (Ephesians 3:20).

So what can you do when you feel like you've failed? You can choose surrender. Instead of falling into the downward spiral of lies and trying to fight defeat on your own, you can choose to believe scripture when it says, "for the Lord your God *is* He who goes with you, to fight for you against your enemies, to save you," (Deuteronomy 20:4). When we fail, God's word reminds us who is the ultimate victor. Remember that through Christ the ultimate victory is ours. We may lose a few battles but the war is already won through the cross of Christ. So when failure tries to settle in and make itself feel final, remember who really has the final say.

reflection

Is there an area of your life where you haven't surrendered to God? What battles are you trying to fight as commander in chief?

Memorize Exodus 14:14. Ask the Lord to help you surrender the battles in your life that you have been fighting on your own.

Search the scriptures and memorize three verses that declare victory over our failures. When you feel like giving up the Holy Spirit will remind you of the truth.

'YOU HAVE SKIRTED
THIS MOUNTAIN
LONG ENOUGH; TURN
NORTHWARD...'

DEUTERONOMY 2:3

I figured if I kept dieting I would eventually lose weight, love my body, and all of my problems would be solved...but God alone is the solution.

CHAPTER TWELVE // STOP CIRCLING THE MOUNTAIN

Have you ever felt like no matter how hard you try that you're getting nowhere? It's a pretty defeating feeling. To work hard at something and feel like you're going in circles is not only discouraging but it can make you feel like you're going crazy.

I had been praying and crying for many months for God to deliver me from my overeating and heal my mind of my distorted body image. I had surrendered the fight to Him and, lo and behold, the Lord gave me direction. God is always faithful. I felt the Lord clearly direct me to stop dieting. But instead of listening to Him, I decided that His way was too difficult. I didn't want to take the hard way. What I didn't realize was that sometimes the only way to the top *is* the hard way.

I was not about to give up my diets. Dieting was a security blanket and I figured if I kept dieting I would eventually lose weight, love my body, and all of my problems would be solved. But God knew that dieting wouldn't and couldn't solve any of my problems. He alone was my solution.

Turns out I was circling the mountain. Have you ever read this verse in Deuteronomy 2:2-3? "And the Lord spoke to me, saying: 'You have skirted this mountain long enough; turn northward.' " That was me! Round and around I skirted that mountain. I finally realized that skirting is actually a lot more exhausting than heading straight up. I had circled the mountain long enough and it was time to trust that Jesus would be with me on the difficult journey up. I threw away my diets and God took me by the hand on this new route up the mountain. It was hard, but we made it.

If you feel like you're going in circles maybe it's time to look up. Throw your map aside and look to Him to be a lamp to your feet and a light to your path. He won't lead you in circles, just get ready for the climb of your life.

reflection

Is there something you know you're supposed to be doing but aren't?

Ask the Holy Spirit to speak to you about how to eat healthy while honoring your body *and* God. Are you holding onto a security blanket instead of fully surrendering to trusting God?

Next time you're faced with a decision regarding your eating habits, choose to honor your body. If you're hungry, eat until you're satisfied. If you're full, stop eating. There's not need to under or over eat when we listen to our bodies. Don't place your trust in a diet plan. Listen to your God given internal GPS when it comes to eating.

UNLESS THE LORD
BUILDS THE HOUSE,
THEY LABOR IN VAIN
WHO BUILD IT...

PSALM 127:1

Healthy is not about seeing changes on the scale or never missing a gym session. It's about seeing yourself in the way that God sees you.

CHAPTER THIRTEEN // THE MASTER ARCHITECT

I know what it's like to work hard at the gym and no matter the physical progress still feel upset with your appearance. Following my own plans lead me to be discouraged with my body, angry when I missed a gym session, and upset when the scale didn't change. The plans in my heart promised to lead me forward but in actuality were leading me nowhere. I still wasn't content.

Psalm 127:1 says, "Unless the Lord builds the house, They labor in vain who build it; Unless the Lord guards the city, The watchman stays awake in vain." This verse applies to every area of our life including being healthy and fit. Before you set off determined to reach your goals, read Proverbs 19:21, "There are many plans in a man's heart, Nevertheless the Lord's counsel - that will stand." Letting God rule over your heart is the first step to walking in His counsel, so be careful about setting out on your own plan to get healthy and fit because you can wind up going around in circles. And circles aren't fun.

Let me remind you of something: what's important to you is important to God. Therefore, He understands your desire to be fit and He knows the best plan to help you get there. His plan might look different than what you imagine. But it is always so much better than our own.

God helped me to rebuild my idea of healthy based on His word. Healthy is not about seeing changes on the scale or never missing a gym session. It's about seeing yourself in the way that God sees you. It's not about just training physically but spiritually too. So it's time to allow the Master architect to draw up the plans. I promise if you let Him, He will not only build you a house but make you a home.

reflection

Think of a time when you "labored in vain". What was so defeating about that experience? What helped you move forward?

Ask God to align the plans in your heart with His will. Ask Him to help you trust in Him.

Memorize Proverbs 19:21. This is a great scripture to keep tucked into your heart. You won't regret committing this to memory when life isn't going according to your plan. Remember this verse and trust that His way is higher.

against
the

THE LORD IS
MERCIFUL
AND GRACIOUS,
SLOW TO ANGER,
AND ABOUNDING
IN MERCY

PSALM 103:8

Voices in your head that are not merciful or gracious aren't coming from Jesus.

CHAPTER FOURTEEN // AGAINST THE VOICES

In my early days of fitness I was listening to all of the wrong voices that made me feel trapped, guilty, and confused. In fact I even started to feel guilty after I ate no matter what it was - healthy or not.

The little voice that talks to you inside of your head, does it talk kindly or is it harsh and demanding? I never used to pay attention to how it sounded, just what it said. I never realized that I could have been listening to a bunch of lies, and you might be too.

God is not the author of condemnation or confusion. He is merciful, gracious, slow to anger, and abounding in mercy (Psalm 103:8). Yet all too often we listen to the lies that come straight into our mind from the enemy. His voice sounds a lot different than the Voice of Truth, and I want you to learn to discern who is who and listen accordingly. Let's have a listen to some of those voices...

If I ate a salad a voice would say, "Why even try? You'll have to eat just lettuce every day for the rest of your life if you want to be thin." Condemning. If I ate a cupcake it would say, "Wow. You gave in, you failed. You're going to have to really work if you want to burn that off." Guilty.

There was no winning whether I ate healthy or not.

Voices that are not merciful or gracious aren't coming from Jesus. When you mess up, listen for the voice that is forgiving, not condemning. When you are victorious, listen for the voice that builds you up instead of tearing you down. You'll know the Holy Spirit's voice because it will always lead you to the cross and you'll know the enemy's voice because it will always drive you away from the cross.

Do not entertain thoughts that have no business being there in the first place. If the voice in your head isn't lovely or kind, don't listen to it. Be still and know that you do not need to listen to all of the voices in your head. There's only one Voice you need to hear from. Learn to tune out all of the loud voices and listen for His loving whispers.

reflection

Do you ever hear that voice in your head that drives you away from the cross? Ask God to help you decipher between His voice of loving conviction versus the enemy's voice of condemnation.

Ask God to help you to retrain your mind to only listen to the thoughts that come from Him. What thoughts come from Him? Read and memorize Psalm 103:8.

The next time you are tempted to condemn yourself for "messing up" on eating healthy say   Psalm 103:8 under your breath. Remind yourself that God does not condemn you and therefore you should not condemn yourself.

DO NOT LOVE THE WORLD
OR THE THINGS IN THE
WORLD. IF ANYONE
LOVES THE WORLD, THE
LOVE OF THE FATHER IS
NOT IN HIM

I JOHN 2:15

When we become consumed by reaching our fitness goals or losing weight, we are seeking the "Kingdom of Self".

CHAPTER FIFTEEN // KINGDOMS OF ME

I know what it's like to feel unhappy with my body. To feel upset with your legs because you wished they were thinner. Or to want abs because it seems that every girl online has them except for you. You're probably not a stranger to that feeling either. To look in the mirror and feel anger towards your physical appearance is probably not foreign to you. Being a girl in today's world means feeling the pressure of striving for some type of external improvement. And I know that if I've faced that pressure that you have too. You're not alone. And I want to push back at those false pressures with some truth.

Here's what Jesus has to say about this world in 1 John 2:15, "Do not love the world or the things in the world. If anyone loves the world, the love of the Father is not in him." Now this does not mean you can't like working out, eating healthy, or even enjoy the physical changes of becoming stronger. The kind of love that is used in this verse is the agape type of love - agape meaning do not value supremely, put your hope in, or find your identity in this world. When we become consumed by reaching our fitness goals or losing weight, we are seeking the "Kingdom of Self". We need to remember that we are to seek first the Kingdom of God and His righteousness (Matthew 6:33) and if we are to firmly stand on the commandments of God we need both feet in the same place. Keep in mind there is everything right with honoring your body by working out and eating healthy. The danger here is allowing your image to become all-consuming and all important.

This world is passing away and so are you. You're either here building up Jesus's kingdom or building up your own, and you cannot do both at the same time. Jesus says to deny yourself pick up your cross and follow Him. How can you deny yourself to serve Jesus when you're serving yourself?

One of the biggest oppositions to the kingdom of Heaven is the kingdom of self. The world tells us girls, "Get thin! Do whatever it takes to be beautiful! Fix this! Fix that! You deserve it! Do it for yourself! You'll be happy when you're better looking!" The Bible is crystal clear when it comes to the world in James 4:4 saying, "Adulterers and adulteresses! Do you not know that friendship with the world is enmity with God? Whoever therefore wants to be a friend of the world makes himself an enemy of God."

I want to be a kingdom builder for the kingdom that will not pass away. My incorruptible inheritance that waits for me in Heaven is far better than the treasures that I can store up here on Earth for myself. Building His kingdom allows you to experience eternal joy in Him rather than temporal happiness in your appearance. Fixing your eyes on Jesus allows you to take your eyes off of the mirror and find your acceptance in the light of Christ's love.

reflection

If you could change something about your body, what would you change? Ask the Lord to help you see that part of yourself the way He sees you. Ask Him to give you His eyes for you.

Ask God to give you a greater love for Him than anything in this world. Memorize 1 John 2:15 and say it to yourself every time you feel fixed on the world.

Go onto all of your social media and unfollow any accounts that make you feel less than or jealous. Make a promise to yourself to only allow your eyes look upon things that uplift and encourage you.

FOR BODILY EXERCISE
PROFITS A LITTLE,
BUT GODLINESS IS
PROFITABLE FOR
ALL THINGS...

1 TIMOTHY 4:8

When we exercise we are
divinely thanking God for the
very breath in our lungs.

CHAPTER SIXTEEN // DOES EXERCISE MATTER TO GOD?

Have you ever set out to do a workout and you feel as if everything in time and space prevents you from actually getting to the gym? Yeah I know that feeling. It's called life. You really do want to workout but day after day goes by and the sun sets on your good intentions. Good intentions don't make for good plans. Our days are determined by our priorities. So how can we prioritize working out? Is it possible to truly honor God by taking care of your body amidst the hustle and bustle of everyday life? Is exercise really even necessary?

I believe when we choose to follow Jesus we are submitting every area of our life over to Him. We commit our souls into His care and let the very Spirit of the living God reside within us. Let me ask you then, and be honest with yourself:

do you believe that God cares if you work out? I'd like to point back to 1 Timothy 4:8, "For bodily exercise profits a little, but godliness is profitable for all things, having promise of the life that now is and of that which is to come." Paul is reminding us here of a higher priority, seeking Jesus. That is, and will always be for the life of the Christian, the top priority. Although, let us not neglect the first part of that verse: bodily exercise profits a little. God created you with muscles, tendons, and a beating heart. Should we disregard exercise as simply an earthly activity? I think not. When we exercise we are divinely thanking God for the very breath in our lungs. We are caring for our inward parts that He created.

So in the chaos of your daily life, can you set aside a little time each day to simply say thank you to God for the gift of your body? Can you honor Him by going for a sunset run? Can you bring glory to Him by making it to the gym? Or simply stretching before bed? Yes and yes! The answer is yes. 1 Corinthians 10:31 says, "Therefore, whether you eat or drink, or whatever you do, do all to the glory of God."

So when we consider each day that is set before us, ask Jesus to lead you and guide you in your plans. Make it of utmost importance to seek Him. Read His word. Pray. And instead of dismissing exercise as something you don't have time for, ask the Lord show you how to plan out some time to glorify Him by moving your God given muscles.

reflection

I want you to be honest with these next few questions. Does exercise matter to *you*? Do you neglect to move your body on a daily basis? Or maybe is exercise too much of a priority to you? Do you elevate it over spending time with God? Ask the Lord to help you find balance and peace in this area of your life.

Ask God to help you do everything to the glory of Him (1 Corinthians 10:31) whether you're working out, eating, or even resting.

Replace your good intentions with a good plan. Write out this week's workouts and rest days. Ask God to help you to commit to it. Trust that He will guide you day by day as you discipline yourself to honor the Lord with your workouts and rest.

FOR YOU WERE
BOUGHT AT A PRICE;
THEREFORE GLORIFY GOD
IN YOUR BODY AND
IN YOUR SPIRIT...

1 CORINTHIANS 6:20

Jesus can fill the hunger inside of you that food will never be able to fill.

CHAPTER SEVENTEEN // PAPER CROWNS

Can you imagine eating 6 pieces of ciabatta bread, an entire box of cereal, and a pint of Ben & Jerry's and still feeling hungry? I've been there. Overeating was a very real problem in my life, and the emotional letdown experienced after a binge was very real too.

I cannot describe the emptiness I felt after a binge. I knew it was not God's design for my body, yet no matter how hard I tried, it seemed as if I could never get out of this destructive habit and viscous cycle. Sometimes the harder we try to control something, the messier things seem to get. This was true for me in the area of eating. When I tried to control my calories and restrict my body from eating, I fell into the pit of an eating disorder.

I wanted to reign over my life. I decided that I knew best for me and that if I wanted to diet that I had every right to. But Paul wrote about the "enemies of Christ" in Philippians 3:18-19. It reads, "For many walk, of whom I have told you often, and now tell you even weeping, *that they are* the enemies of the cross of Christ: whose end *is* destruction, whose god *is their* belly, and *whose* glory *is* in their shame - who set their mind on earthly things."

When we elevate earthly desires, such as being thin, above the King of Kings we are sinning against Him. Listen to me closely. I understand the bondage of an eating disorder. I know that food addiction is a real thing because I have experienced it. But I am careful to admit and call out my problem for what it was - sin. I desired being skinny above Jesus. And I suffered the consequences of that sin by developing binge eating disorder.

Giving our lives to Jesus means giving Him permission to reign over every area of our lives. This includes eating. When we sin we are playing king and figuratively speaking putting on paper crowns. We are saying that our authority is greater than the ultimate authority. In 1 Corinthians Paul reminds us that we were bought at a price. Therefore we are to glorify God in our body which is His. It's time to take off our paper crowns and joyfully submit to the rule of the King.

If you are struggling with an eating disorder take hope in this: Jesus can rescue you. He is mighty to save you from bondage and break every chain in your life. Think about this: Jesus reconciled us to God in order to save us from eternal separation from Him. How much more is he able to rescue you from your addiction or disorder? The power of sin and addiction is broken in our lives through the blood of Jesus. We are victorious through the cross of Christ. And in every area of your life you are more than a conqueror through Him. He can fill the hunger inside of you that food will never be able to fill.

reflection

For a long time being thin was more important to me than being free. Do you feel this way now? Ask the Lord to search your heart and examine your motives in this area.

Ask God to break every chain in your life that is keeping you from walking in freedom with Him. Pray every day that Jesus will transform your mind and free your thoughts from anything that is guiding you away from truth.

Start each day by declaring victory over yourself. Before you get out of bed say, "Today I am walking in freedom through the victory that Jesus has given to me. I am beautifully and wonderfully made by Him. I am no longer a slave to anything, but I am free in Christ to live outside of the power of sin. Even if I mess up today, I know that God loves me and accepts me and therefore I will love and accept myself. Today I choose grace. Today I choose joy. Today I choose forgiveness. Today I choose to walk in victory."

growi
in all

AND WE KNOW THAT
ALL THINGS WORK
TOGETHER FOR GOOD
TO THOSE WHO
LOVE GOD...

ROMANS 8:28

Remember that sore today
means strong tomorrow.

CHAPTER EIGHTEEN // GROWING IN ALL THINGS

If you have ever been extremely sore after an intense workout you've probably experienced this bittersweet feeling: happiness that you're getting stronger yet at the same time you feel the achy pain of the muscles you just worked in the gym. If you've ever tried sitting down after an intense leg workout, you know what I'm talking about!

It's kind of like reaching the top of a mountain. It's hard and you might be a little sore once you reach the top, but it's all worth it in the end. Just look at that view! I love mountaintop experiences— it's refreshing up there. But the fruit of our labor is not produced on the mountain top. Fruit is grown in the depths of the valley.

My eating disorder was spent in the valley. It was hard. It was dark. I felt the weight of my sin bearing down on me. I had wanted to be thin so badly that I was willing to go down whatever path necessary. I didn't know I would be leading myself into a valley for many years. Yet in those years I trusted in God's Word that, " ...all things work together for good to those who love God, to those who are the called according to *His* purpose," (Romans 8:28). Jesus was growing me and we grow to where we need to go. I had to lay down my desire to have a perfect body and grow in trusting that the Lord would be faithful to deliver me.

Even in the lowest parts of life, God will grow you for your own good. Don't give up. Press on and press in because you will reap a harvest if you do not give up (Galatians 6:9) Remember that sore today means strong tomorrow. Don't be discouraged because of the rain, you'll get future flowers for your present pain.

reflection

Do you feel as if you're in a valley right now? Are you having trouble seeing the goodness of God in the midst of the low parts of life?

Ask God to help you to see His redemptive power in your circumstances.

Memorize Romans 8:28, "And we know that all things work together for good to those who love God, to those who are the called according to *His* purpose."

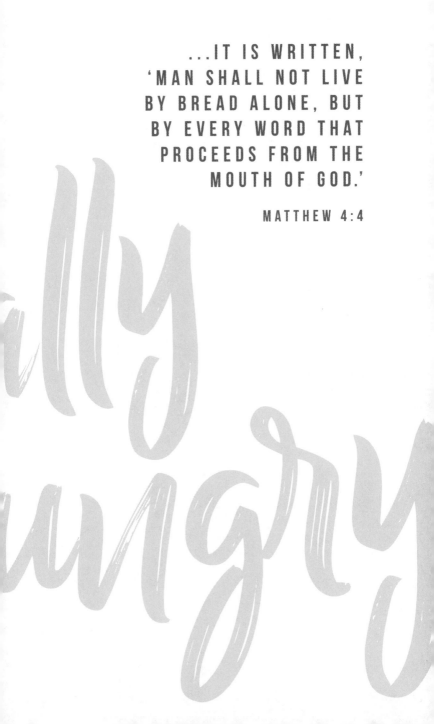

...IT IS WRITTEN,
'MAN SHALL NOT LIVE
BY BREAD ALONE, BUT
BY EVERY WORD THAT
PROCEEDS FROM THE
MOUTH OF GOD.'

MATTHEW 4:4

Nourishing your body and neglecting to feed your spirit is going to leave you hungry.

CHAPTER NINETEEN // SPIRITUALLY HUNGRY

If we want to have a strong body we need to continually eat healthy food. If we want to grow strong in the Lord we need to continually feed on His word. Jesus said in Matthew 4:4, "It is written, 'Man shall not live by bread alone, but by every word that proceeds from the mouth of God.' " So let me ask you this, do you really believe what Jesus is saying about another kind of food?

When I get super hungry I can get super angry. Hangry, you know? Typically I don't allow myself to get to such a miserable state. I eat. I snack. And when I feel the hunger coming on I stop whatever I'm doing and my attention is on nothing but getting food. Yet how often do we stop whatever we're doing and pray? Or wake up every single morning to feed on God's word?

When you're trying to reach your fitness goals, you'll be tempted to focus on just eating the right food and exercising. But nourishing your body and neglecting to feed your spirit is going to leave you hungry. You can't live on protein bars alone! You must care for your spirit by feeding on the word of God. Jesus said there is another kind of nourishment we need that can't come from food. That means feeding on the word of God. You have to pick up your Bible in order to not starve your soul.

It's time to start nourishing the right way. That means some mornings you'll be eating your breakfast with Matthew. Other days you might be dining with Luke. Whatever you do, don't forget that you can't grow in strength without the right nourishment. You can't give it your all during a workout if you haven't eaten all day. Trust me, I learned that the hard way. It's called fainting. Your body needs food. And your soul needs Jesus.

reflection

Are you starving spiritually right now? Have you made a daily commitment to reading God's Word and not living on bread alone?

Ask God to help you to see the supremacy of God's Word in your life. In your quest for being healthy ask Him to show you just how important it is to feed on the bread of life.

Instead of rushing off in the morning – whether it's to work or to workout – carve out that sacred space to just sit and read the Bible. You know how you grab a banana or blend up a smoothie to take on the go when your mornings are rushed? Well the same thing applies to your spiritual nourishment. There are some days that you're running late or just don't have a lot of time. Bible on audiobook? Oh yes. Jesus is always there, ready to listen.

YOU SHALL
HAVE NO
OTHER GODS
BEFORE ME

EXODUS 20:3

"In all your ways
acknowledge Him,
and He shall direct your paths."
Proverbs 3:6

CHAPTER TWENTY // FOLLOW THE MAP

I dieted for years. You know where it got me? Absolutely nowhere. Well actually it did get me somewhere. It lead me into disordered thinking and created in me an unhealthy relationship with food. I even gained weight. Let's just say it took me where I didn't want to go and did a lot more harm than help.

God has created our bodies in a magnificent way. He has given us an internal roadmap to our health and it's right inside of us. It's called being hungry and being full. When we listen to those internal signals we can never go wrong. Yet all too often we seek out external controls such as dieting. Counting calories, fat, carbs, protein, and the list goes on. How do you think people stayed healthy and fit before we figured out what a calorie was? I guarantee the people who lived 300 years ago weren't counting macros or weighing their food. They ate when they were hungry and stopped when they were full.

Instead of trusting in how God created us, we try to take control of our food by thinking that we know best. Dieting invariably leads to unhealthy behavior, like not eating when you're hungry because you're over your daily calorie limit. Or not eating fruit because it's too high in sugar. Or skimping on your avocado because it's too high in fat.

Dieting created idolatry in my heart. Jesus does not want to compete with anything or anyone in your heart. He wants your heart to be after Him. He is lovingly jealous for you. Remember when we're sinning that means we're playing king and wearing our paper crowns, thinking that our authority is above the King of Kings. He created you, don't you think He knows more about you than you? Therefore He knows what's best for you, even when it comes to food.

Throw away your map. This requires trust in the one who put the hunger inside of you. Recognize it is a gift from God to feel hungry and satisfied. I want to save you from following the dieting map because it won't lead you up the mountain it will lead you in circles around the mountain. So trust that your Creator made you right and His direction is worth following.

reflection

Are you currently dieting or disregarding your internal feelings of hungry and full? Maybe you don't eat when you're hungry because you've hit your macro limit. Or you continue eating even after you're stuffed because you "won't ever eat anything unhealthy again." How do you feel about this way of living?

Ask God to help you to honor your internal road map. To listen and to follow it means to follow after the way He designed us.

Next time you're hungry eat until you're satisfied. When you're full, honor your body by saving the next bite for later. Ask God to show you the best way for you to eat.

salad
cho

...DO YOU NOT PERCEIVE
THAT WHATEVER ENTERS A
MAN FROM OUTSIDE CANNOT
DEFILE HIM, BECAUSE
IT DOES NOT ENTER HIS
HEART BUT HIS STOMACH,
AND IS ELIMINATED, THUS
PURIFYING ALL FOODS?

MARK 7:18-19

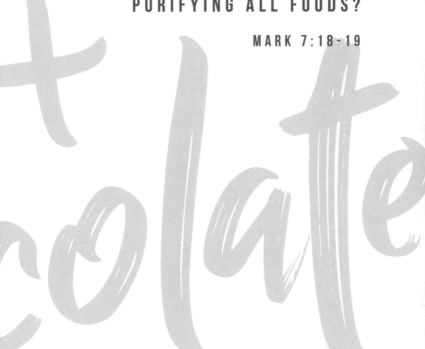

"All things are lawful for me,
but not all things are helpful;
all things are lawful for me, but
not all things edify."
1 Corinthians 10:23

CHAPTER TWENTY-ONE // GOD MADE SALADS...AND CHOCOLATE

Let's get real. Eating healthy does not mean never eating chocolate again. Unfortunately I used to think it did. Maybe you read that and laughed, you know that's unrealistic, yet you feel guilty every time you even *think* about eating chocolate. Well my friend, I'd like to remind you that the God who created the leaves in the salad we eat is the same God who created the cocoa beans that make chocolate.

I believe in the wonderful balance of moderation. What if we only ever read the book of Leviticus? We'd never understand the grace of God pertaining to our sin. But what if we only ever read the book of Galatians? We might feel free to walk in sin by abusing God's grace. That's why we have a balance in the Bible of grace and truth. We need both. Just like in a healthy diet you need balance.

What if you only ever ate vegetables? You never ate any fruit or had any protein. You'd probably not feel very well. That's why we eat a variety of different foods. You understand that you need a variety of wholesome foods to create balance, but what about those fresh out of the oven cookies that you love?

One of my favorite things about the Bible is that it answers our biggest and hardest questions and sometimes even our silly and small questions. Reminding us that God cares for the details of our lives. In Mark 7:18-19 Jesus says, "...Do you not perceive that whatever enters a man from outside cannot defile him, because it does not enter his heart but his stomach, and is eliminated, *thus* purifying all foods?" So there you have it. That cookie isn't going to defile you.

Your body is the temple of the Holy Spirit. And when you stop dieting and start listening to your internal signals you will know that excessive chocolate or excessive sugar is not healthy. Proverbs 25:27 says, "*It is* not good to eat much honey; So to seek one's own glory *is not* glory." But depriving yourself from any and all chocolate ever, isn't healthy either! That's going to make you want the chocolate even more and create obsessive thoughts about food. And chocolate isn't worth obsessing over. So eat some chocolate! But don't obsess over it and don't feel guilty for eating it either. It's called balance and it's a wonderful thing to eat, bon appétit.

reflection

Do you ever feel guilty after eating something sweet? Maybe you feel as if you have an all or nothing type of attitude regarding sweets?

Ask God to help you to learn to stop obsessing and feeling guilty regarding sweets.

Next time you want to enjoy a sweet treat remember 1 Corinthians 10:23, "All things are lawful for me, but not all things are helpful; all things are lawful for me, but not all things edify." Enjoy your sweet treat without guilt, and remember that 10 cookies is over indulging!

I WILL PRAISE YOU, FOR
I AM FEARFULLY AND
WONDERFULLY MADE;
MARVELOUS ARE YOUR
WORKS, AND THAT MY SOUL
KNOWS VERY WELL

PSALM 139:14

When I'm crying because the mirror is making me feel less than and alone, I quote Psalm 139:14, "I will praise You, for I am fearfully and wonderfully made; Marvelous are Your works and that my soul knows very well."

CHAPTER TWENTY-TWO // UNIQUE

If you have ever struggled with looking in the mirror and been unhappy with the reflection you see, you're not alone. There have been countless nights that my heart felt the hopelessness of ever measuring up to the perfect image in my head. Maybe you've felt that exact same hopelessness too. Our insecurities are not rare. Yet at the same time I felt like no one understood how I felt. And I'm sure you feel that same way too. There is not one person on this planet who is just like you, in your situation, with your background. Same goes for me. But on the other side of it there is another women out there looking in the mirror with tears streaming down her face feeling insecure with her figure. We aren't unique and yet at the same time we absolutely are.

So where does that leave us when we're crying in the middle of the night feeling more alone than ever? Although others around us experience the same type of pain, they cannot experience *your* pain. So in essence we all suffer alone. The enemy wants us to believe that not even God knows your suffering. That's where we have to draw a line in the sand. Yes we are strangely unique in our pain, but there is no pain that Jesus doesn't perfectly understand. That is our hope in our aloneness, that we are in fact never alone with Jesus. Hebrews 4:15 reminds us, "For we do not have a High Priest who cannot sympathize with our weaknesses, but was in all *points* tempted as *we are, yet* without sin." The weakness here is the temptation to believe the lies of the enemy that we are alone, we aren't good enough, and that our joy lies in perfecting our image. We need to remind ourselves that God is with us, He is Emmanuel. Therefore, He understands our pain and the temptation to give into the lies. He not only empathizes with our pain but provides a solution to that pain.

Jesus fully knows who you are and where you are. He is the one who has never left your side. The one who catches every tear you cry and the one will wipe them all away one day. So when I'm crying because the mirror is making me feel less than and alone, I quote Psalm 139:14, "I will praise You, for I am fearfully and wonderfully made; Marvelous are Your works, And that my soul knows very well." I have found the closeness of God to be very real when I quote scripture. Psalm 119:11 says, "Your word I have hidden in my heart, That I might not sin against You." So in those dark nights that I feel alone, I have found a friend in hiding scripture in my heart. It is the comfort and the remedy that my soul needs.

reflection

Do you believe it's possible to love your body? What hinders you from believing this?

Ask God right now, to help you see yourself as beautiful and to stop believing the lie that your joy is only found in the perfect body. Perfect love and joy is found in Jesus!

Next time you feel alone and upset with your body take a moment to really lay your worries at the feet of Jesus. Don't give a half-hearted prayer. Tell Him your deepest fears and give Him this heavy burden to carry.

the roa
mode

...LET US LAY ASIDE EVERY
WEIGHT, AND THE SIN
WHICH SO EASILY ENSNARES
US, AND LET US RUN WITH
ENDURANCE THE RACE
THAT IS SET BEFORE US

HEBREWS 12:1

"Beloved, I beg you as sojourners and pilgrims, abstain from fleshly lusts which war against your soul."
1 Peter 2:11

CHAPTER TWENTY-THREE // THE ROAD OF MODERATION

The smell of chocolate chip cookies baking in the oven is arguably the best smell in the world. Actually that's not up for debate. It is the best smell. The anticipation is in the air and those warm, delicious, gooey cookies are about to be ready. But you just got back from the gym. You're tired, you're hungry, and those cookies smell good. Really good. You just had a killer workout though! What to do, what to do?

First understand that there is nothing wrong with eating a cookie. Even after a workout. I don't care what a diet says, you can eat that cookie and enjoy every bite free of guilt. But if you're anything like me and have struggled with food addiction, you know it might not be that simple.

I had a food addiction. Especially to anything sugary, sweet, or associated with the word "carb". My overeating was keeping me in major bondage and I knew that I could not just eat one cookie. I couldn't even eat just two. I knew once I started I wouldn't be able to stop. I was in bondage and had no self-control. Therefore, before I could enjoy cookies in moderation without overeating I knew I had to develop a healthy relationship with food again. I had to come to the conclusion to give up sugary food.

Please understand I didn't decide to permanently give up on eating cookies. I decided to abstain from sugar for a period of time. I eat cookies now and enjoy them in moderation; it's wonderful, delicious, and freeing all at the same time. Understand that it took a long time for me to heal my relationship with food, with lots of trial and error. But before I was able to enjoy sweets in moderation, I had to give up the foods that tempted me to overeat.

1 Peter 2:11 says, "Beloved, I beg *you* as sojourners and pilgrims, abstain from fleshly lusts which war against the soul," Eating one cookie for me, was much more than just eating a cookie. Indulging in desserts was waging war against my soul. It was hindering me from caring for my body, the Temple of the Holy Spirit, in a controlled way. I ignored my God-given gift of hungry and satisfied, and would continue to eat long after I was full to the point of being sick. And that was reason enough for me to give up sugar for a period of time. I trusted that God was going to deliver me from my bondage, and in the meantime I needed to abstain from anything that would wage war against my soul.

It's not about not eating sugar. Or even giving up sweets. It's about recognizing the things that are weighing you down. Maybe it's something different for you. Whatever it is remember that the Bible says in Hebrews 12:1 to, "let us lay aside every weight, and the sin which so easily ensnares us, and let us run with endurance the race that is set before us."

Eating cookies is not a sin. But obsessing about food and idolizing my appearance was. Usually the reason I would binge on sweets was due to the fact that I typically didn't eat enough during the day, which is the furthest thing from honoring my body and traces back to idolizing my image. Anything that's weighing you down needs to be thrown off. Be encouraged because you can do all things through Jesus, He will give you strength!

reflection

Is there something in your life that you feel is weighing you down? What does it look like to throw that thing out of your life?

Ask God to show you what needs to be thrown off in your life. Ask Him to give you the guidance and strength that comes from Him.

Next time you're tempted to binge or overeat, take a step back. Sit down and simply pray and ask Jesus to help you. Sit and just breathe and pray until you calm down. Know that when you do this every time you're struggling God will be faithful to help you! Matthew 7:7 says, "Ask, and it will be given to you; seek, and you will find; knock, and it will be opened to you."

THEREFORE, IF ANYONE IS
IN CHRIST, HE IS A NEW
CREATION; OLD THINGS
HAVE PASSED AWAY;
BEHOLD, ALL THINGS
HAVE BECOME NEW

2 CORINTHIANS 5:17

Jesus died for you no matter what you weigh. Your value has no ties to the scale.

Jesus died for you no matter what you weigh. Your value has no ties to the scale.

You can honor God by working out and eating healthy, but you cannot earn your value from doing those things. You are already stamped with God's approval, and it doesn't come from anything you do or have done.

Remember when Satan tempted Jesus? He said to Jesus in Matthew 4:3, " '*If* You are the Son of God, command that these stones become bread.' " The Greek word for "if" that is being used here is translated to "indeed." So Satan was really saying, "*Indeed* You are the Son of God, command that these stones become bread." You see, Satan wasn't doubting Jesus' identity, he just wanted Jesus to prove His identity. He was basically saying, "You need to do something of real worth to prove who you are."

We experience this same temptation every day. We too have an identity in Christ and Satan knows that fully well. He's not going to doubt our identity, he's just going to suck us into the trap of always trying to prove it. Our identity is a free gift from Christ. We are the beloved of God not by something we have done, but in spite of all that we have done. The Gospel is God's gift to us. We have His full approval in Christ. No matter what, we are his beloved daughters. We cannot earn it. It's already ours!

The enemy is always going to try to keep you striving. So when you're tempted to try to prove your worth to God, others, or even yourself remember you don't need to fall into that trap! We are accepted by God only because of Jesus. All we need to do is to accept the work that His Son did on the cross. Your worth is not in your weight. Your worth is found in Jesus Christ. 2 Corinthians 5:17 says, "Therefore, if anyone *is* in Christ, *he is* a new creation; old things have passed away; behold, all things have become new."

Choose to nourish your body and work out by God's grace; not in order to gain God's approval but because you already have God's approval.

reflection

Do you find yourself trying to prove your worth to God? What area of your life needs a fresh receiving of God's grace?

How should you live if you're "in Christ"? Ask Jesus to show you what that looks like in your own life and in your own heart. Today is the day to start living out of your God-given value instead of trying to prove it.

Memorize 2 Corinthians 5:17, "Therefore, if anyone is in Christ, *he is* a new creation; old things have passed away; behold, all things have become new."

BUT WHOEVER DRINKS OF
THE WATER THAT I
SHALL GIVE HIM WILL
NEVER THIRST...

JOHN 4:14

With Jesus when you give
up the desire for lesser things,
you're never losing anything.

The enemy lied to me for years promising satisfaction with myself if... *If* I did something to earn it. *If* I lost weight. *If* I had a better body. I had "if'd" my life away. I believed the enemy because my soul was starving from the truth. The more we have spiritual nourishment the less we're thrown off by the things we don't have.

Take a look with me at what Jesus said to the woman at the well. As she was drawing Him a drink of water, Jesus said to her in John 4:14, "but whoever drinks of the water that I shall give him will never thirst. But the water that I shall give him will become in him a fountain of water springing up into everlasting life." Pretty bold statement. Yet those bold words challenge us to be bold in believing what He says to be true. Understand first that Jesus is not saying that if you drink from Him that He will satisfy you by giving you everything you want in this life. No. He's calling you to a better thing: eternal life and freedom in Him!

Ask yourself do you really believe that Jesus can permanently quench your thirst? Is the gospel enough to satisfy you? You will never thirst again when you find your worth in Christ. Your worth then is not found in what size jeans you wear or how fit you look. It won't be determined by the accomplishments you reach or even the biggest setbacks you face. The righteousness of Christ says you are perfectly loved and accepted in the Beloved - no matter what. This is good news because that gives us victory over striving. I don't like working for things that will ultimately run me dry. So stop burning out trying to reach for things that will never satisfy. You don't have to do better or be more. Just look more carefully and clearly at Jesus. With Jesus when you give up the desire for lesser things, you're never losing anything. In fact you will lose nothing and gain it all.

reflection

What area of your life are you striving for satisfaction in? Your body image? Your job? What does it look like to rest in Jesus in those areas?

Ask Jesus to help you to be fully satisfied in *Him* rather than striving for satisfaction.

There can be many areas in your life that try to keep you from believing that you can be fully satisfied in Jesus. List out those areas and then next to each of them write a scripture that invites truth into that area. This will not only help you to identify weak areas in your life, but it will help you to strengthen them with the power of God's word.

incorru

RATHER LET IT BE THE
HIDDEN PERSON OF
THE HEART, WITH THE
INCORRUPTIBLE BEAUTY OF
A GENTLE AND QUIET SPIRIT,
WHICH IS VERY PRECIOUS IN
THE SIGHT OF GOD

1 PETER 3:4

A beautiful face cannot compare to a beautiful heart.

CHAPTER TWENTY-SIX // INCORRUPTIBLE BEAUTY

Let's be real, I want to be confident with myself and I know you do too. We like beautiful things and we want to be beautiful. But most of us spend our time fixing up our outward self rather than working on our inward self, even though we know intuitively it's what's inside that counts. So how do we balance feeling beautiful without being totally consumed by our appearance? How do we find the inner peace with our outer selves? I wrestled with this for a long time. And here's what God's word says about it:

1 Peter 3:3-4 says, "Do not let your adornment be merely outward - arranging the hair, wearing gold, or putting on *fine* apparel - rather *let it be* the hidden person of the heart, with the incorruptible *beauty* of a gentle and quiet spirit, which is very precious in the sight of God." This tells me that if there's an incorruptible beauty then there's also a corruptible beauty. When we focus on merely

the outward like the verse says, we are focusing on improving our corruptible beauty. There's nothing wrong with a pretty face, and don't get me wrong I do love my makeup, but there's something deeper here. A beautiful face cannot compare to a beautiful heart. Jesus is talking about an eternal beauty here that has nothing to do with fixing our hair or wearing cute clothes.

The real beauty that is incorruptible and eternal is only found in the heart. So when we spend more time and place greater importance on our outward self rather than developing a gentle and quiet spirit, we're not going to attain real, true beauty. It's not going to last. Some of the most beautiful women I've ever met have grey hair and plenty of wisdom-made wrinkles.

I'd rather drink a delicious beverage out of an ugly mug than be sipping on expired milk in fine china. I bet you would too. So when it comes down to it Jesus is right: don't let your adornment merely be outward.

You can work on the outward, sure. Putting on makeup and a beautiful dress makes me feel beautiful on the outside. So does keeping a consistent workout routine to stay fit and in shape. There's nothing wrong with that. But let's not let it end there. If it's more important to you to make it to the gym than it is to meet with Jesus, it's time to reevaluate your standard of beauty.

reflection

How much time do you spend on your inward beauty in comparison to your outward? Do you feel it could use some balancing?

Ask God to help you to place a much greater importance on your inward beauty.

Make a habit of daily reading your Bible and talking to the Lord, just as you regularly wake up get dressed and put on your makeup. Make spending time with Jesus apart of your regular beauty routine.

#ble8

REJOICE AND BE
EXCEEDINGLY
GLAD, FOR GREAT
IS YOUR REWARD
IN HEAVEN...

MATTHEW 5:12

My idea of blessed used to be having etched abs, wearing the smallest jeans, having the longest hair, and wearing the cutest clothes. But my idea was far from lining up with Jesus's.

CHAPTER TWENTY-SEVEN // #BLESSED

Sometimes I'll see a super fit girl online and think, "Wow she is so blessed! Look at what God has given her – a perfect body! I would be happy if only I had what she has." We assume that blessed is the one who has it all. The one who is celebrated and elevated. And we want to be "blessed" too. But what if being blessed is not what you think?

The Sermon on the Mount is one of the most famous passages in the Bible and yet we disregard it almost every day by comparing our lives to the lives of the "blessed" people we know. Jesus says blessed are the poor in spirit, the ones who mourn, and the ones who are persecuted. Whoa, whoa, whoa! The persecuted? The ones who mourn? What about the girl on Instagram with 1 million followers and rock hard abs? Isn't she blessed? Our definition of blessed is a little different than Jesus's. Ok a lot different.

Let's look a little closer at Matthew 5:3-4, "Blessed *are* the poor in spirit, For theirs is the kingdom of heaven. Blessed *are* those who mourn, For they shall be comforted." When we look at other people's earthly gains and think that God has blessed them, we are completely missing it. Jesus finishes by saying in Matthew 5:12, "Rejoice and be exceedingly glad, for great *is* your reward in heaven, for so they persecuted the prophets who were before you." Happy are the ones who rejoice during the heartache here on earth because they know their eternal reward is on heaven's horizon.

My idea of blessed used to be having etched abs, wearing the smallest jeans, having the longest hair, and wearing the cutest clothes. But my idea was far from lining up with Jesus's. The difference is mine was focused on the temporal and His is focused on the eternal. That sets us free from looking at earthly "blessings" and thinking that that person has it made. Because of Jesus, we are truly blessed!

Why do you think Jesus's definition of blessing is so different from our own? Why is the real definition important for us to understand?

Ask God to help you to see what true blessing is. To what extent do you recognize God's blessings in your life? What are some ways you believe God has blessed you?

Write down some ways you believe God has blessed you. When you wake up read this list as a daily reminder that God is faithful and you are blessed beyond measure!

ALL THINGS ARE
LAWFUL FOR ME,
BUT ALL THINGS
ARE NOT HELPFUL...

1 CORINTHIANS 6:12

Freedom doesn't give us the right to do whatever we want to do, it gives us the right to do what we ought to do.

CHAPTER TWENTY-EIGHT // THE CHOICE IS YOURS

We are free in Jesus to eat and enjoy food, but should we abuse that freedom and only eat junk food just because we're free to do so? I don't think that's helpful or beneficial. We must be honest with ourselves to see that freedom really isn't free. Our freedom came at a high cost to God - sacrificing His Son for us. We were bought with the highest price of Jesus' perfect blood. When we understand the price Jesus paid for our freedom we are less likely to abuse our liberties.

Yet for so many years I felt like I didn't have a choice when it came to food. It felt like food had control over me, rather than me having control over my food. I was locked inside of a cell and I had the key to unlock the door. Freedom was in the palm of my hand and I had no idea. I had abused my freedom to choose food and because of that I became enslaved to it. I thought that controlling every calorie and monitoring every ounce of food that went into my body was walking in my freedom. Yet in my freedom I unknowingly walked straight into bondage.

God in Christ has given us freedom from the bondage of sin and because of Him we have incredible liberty. 1 Corinthians 6:12 says, "All things are lawful for me, but all things are not helpful. All things are lawful for me, but I will not be brought under the power of any."

This verse helps us both to understand that while we are free to do what we want, not everything we do will be good for us. In fact the end of that verse shows us that with great freedom comes great responsibility. We can indeed be brought under the power of things if we abuse our freedom to choose. Just like when I started dieting I thought I had control over my food but that's exactly when it started to take control of me.

The good news is that there is good news. The choice is, in fact, yours. All things are allowed but remember that not everything is beneficial. See, it's ok for me to choose to diet but that's not beneficial for me. I become obsessed with the gift of food rather than the Giver of food.

Freedom doesn't give us the right to do whatever we want to do, it gives us the right to do what we ought to do. God has given us a great gift in choosing our foods and we should use that rather than abuse that freedom.

You do not have to be enslaved to food. Lecrae said, "Freedom in Christ allows you to control the desires that once controlled you."

In what area of your life are you choosing to do something but it might not be good for you? Do you find yourself abusing this freedom?

Commit to memory Galatians 5:13-14, "For you, brethren, have been called to liberty; only do not *use* liberty as an opportunity for the flesh, but through love serve one another. For all the law is fulfilled in one word, *even* in this: "You shall love your neighbor as yourself."

Put into your own words what freedom is. What light does 1 Corinthians 6:12 shed on true freedom?

IF IT IS POSSIBLE,
AS MUCH AS
DEPENDS ON YOU,
LIVE PEACEABLY
WITH ALL MEN

ROMANS 12:18

Jesus died to free us from the law and make us alive in Christ through grace and forgiveness.

CHAPTER TWENTY-NINE // FREEDOM HERE, THERE, & EVERYWHERE

Colossians 2:16-17 says, "So let no one judge you in food or in drink, or regarding a festival or a new moon or sabbaths, which are a shadow of things to come, but the substance is of Christ, which are a shadow of things to come, but the substance is of Christ." There are those today who still desire to judge you and I. Especially concerning healthy eating. Everyone has different ideas and opinions and the sad thing is that everyone thinks they're right.

There are many people who take Bible verses and twist them to make their own opinion seem right. But here's the thing: Jesus had no patience for legalism. Jesus died to free us from the law and make us alive in Christ through grace and forgiveness despite what we do. We need to remember this especially when it comes to healthy eating. You are free to choose what you want to eat, and your health journey is your own personal story between you and a personal God! This is the same for your neighbor or friend who might also be struggling with body image, eating, idolatry, and shame. They are on a personal journey navigated by an all-knowing God. We can become so consumed with our own healthy eating that we start to think our way is the only way - especially if it worked and we received healing, our best intentions to help others with solutions can sometimes turn into judgment if we are not careful. James 4:12 says, "There is one Lawgiver, who is able to save and to destroy. Who are you to judge another?"

Let God guide you to health and healing. Whether you decide to eat vegetarian, vegan, pescatarian, paleo, and the list goes on, you are free to choose what's healthy for you and unique for your body! But don't let your decision and your conviction cause you to look down on others in judgment. The Bible makes it clear that there is not one way of eating. Whether we eat or drink we are to bring glory to the Lord.

Romans 14:2-10 says, "For one believes he may eat all things, but he who is weak eats only vegetables. Let not him who eats despise him who does not eat, and let not him who does not eat judge him who eats; for God has received him. Who are you to judge another's servant? To his own master he stands or falls. Indeed, he will be made to stand, for God is able to make him stand. One person esteems *one* day above another; another esteems every day *alike*. Let each be fully convinced in his own mind. He who observes the day, observes *it* to the Lord; and he who does not observe the day, to the Lord he does not observe *it*. He who eats, eats to the Lord, for he gives God thanks; and he who does not eat, to the Lord he does not eat, and gives God thanks. For none of us lives to himself, and no one dies to himself. For if we live, we live to the Lord; and if we die, we die to the Lord. Therefore, whether we live or die, we are the Lord's. For to this end Christ died and rose and lived again, that He might be Lord of both the dead and the living. But why do you judge your brother? Or why do you show contempt for your brother? For we shall all stand before the judgment seat of Christ."

How thankful I am for the freedom Christ gives me in every area of my life including food. Just as there's not one right way to exercise, there's not one right way to eat. You are free to take care of your body in a way that works for you. Remember that when you take care of your body and choose to be healthy, you are directly honoring the Holy Spirit who lives within you. In the same way the Holy Spirit led you in your personal journey, trust that He will lead your neighbor or friend in the same!

reflection

Choosing to take care of your body physically is a good thing and it's also a benefit to your spiritual health. How are the two connected?

What does it look like to choose health in your own personal life? Ask God to specifically lead you in this area if you need guidance. If there is a person or friend that you are concerned about their health, pray the Holy Spirit would move in their hearts and lead them to greater victory.

Consider Romans 14: 2-10. Put into your own words what you think this means for you personally today.

as He
se

FOR YOU ARE A HOLY PEOPLE TO
THE LORD YOUR GOD; THE LORD
YOUR GOD HAS CHOSEN YOU TO BE
A PEOPLE FOR HIMSELF, A SPECIAL
TREASURE ABOVE ALL THE PEOPLES
ON THE FACE OF THE EARTH

DEUTERONOMY 7:6

He can rescue you from the lie that a "perfect body" will make you happy. You're already perfect in His eyes.

CHAPTER THIRTY // AS HE SEES YOU

Desiring a perfect image will leave you empty and exhausted. Desiring to be a reflection of His image will fill your soul in a way you never thought was possible. When you seek to perfect your image you will strive for earthly perfection but when you strive to reflect His image you will find rest in your imperfections.

God isn't looking for the one who gets to the gym every day. He's not looking for the perfect healthy eater. He's not looking for the strong. He's looking for you. Right where you're at right now. You don't need to come to Him with your life perfectly together. Come to Him as you are.

If you are struggling with seeing yourself as beautiful, try seeing yourself as God sees you. Maybe you don't know how to do that. The truth is that you are loved so much that Jesus gave His life for you. When I was in the middle of my eating disorder I had someone at my church pray over me and God used his prayer to change my life. As he prayed he told me to picture Jesus on the cross. I want you to do that now. Picture Him hanging on the cross with nails in His hands, dying for you right where you're at right now. He did so willingly, out of love. He loves you. He accepts you. Know that He looks at you and sees you as spotless. Even when you choose to focus on your flaws, He never will. He can rescue you from the lie that a "perfect body" will make you happy. You're already perfect in His eyes.

Dig into the word of God and find the words that Jesus says about you. Did you know He knows how many hairs are on your head (Luke 12:7)? If He cares and knows such a minor thing about you, do you not think He cares about the major things about you? He sees everything about you and He loves you.

Today commit to seeing yourself and the women around you through the lens of Christ: holy, adopted, blameless, perfect, beautiful, wonderfully made, handcrafted, and unique. He sees you and He has saved you. You are beautiful because He says so. Deuteronomy 7:6 says, "For you *are* a holy people to the Lord your God; the Lord your God has chosen you to be a people for Himself, a special treasure above all the peoples on the face of the earth." A special treasure. That's you! And what a delight to know the one who has never spoken anything but truth, has spoken words of beauty over you.

reflection

Sometimes it's easy to think that God doesn't really care about little problems or internal struggles. Did you know that God's thoughts for you outnumber the grains of sand? If He has that many thoughts about you, you bet that He cares about every single area of your life. Have you ever withheld talking to God about your insecurities because you thought He didn't care?

Ask God to give you His eyes for you. When you look into the mirror view yourself through the lens of Jesus' love for you. He loves every part of you – He made you.

Moving forward this is my prayer over you and your life: 3 John 1:2, "Beloved, I pray that you may prosper in all things and be in health, just as your soul prospers." Commit this scripture to memory and tuck it into your heart. It's one of my favorites, and I hope it will be yours too.

My Friend,

Remember: this battle is the Lord's!

If you have looked in the mirror and felt no worth, remember who paid it all for you. Take your eyes off of the mirror and fix them on Jesus. Because of the cross you are robed in His righteousness, a free and priceless gift that He has given you through His precious blood which gives you immeasurable worth. That's what the gospel does for us, it presents the only reliable foundation of self-evaluation through the perfect mirror of the Word of God.

Look closely and carefully at Jesus. That's the only place where you can see your true worth - not in the reflection of a mirror. Don't go looking for your identity. You've already been given an eternal identity through Jesus and you don't have to seek out anything but the scriptures to discover that.

I'll leave with with these verses that have helped me. I pray that they will encourage and lift you up on the journey ahead: " 'O our God, will You not judge them? For we have no power against this great multitude that is coming against us; nor do we know what to do, but our eyes are upon You.'...Thus says the Lord to you: 'Do not be afraid nor dismayed because of this great multitude, for the battle is not yours, but God's.' " 2 Chronicles 20:12 and 15.

I want to leave you with the assurance that God is faithful. He delivered me and I know that He will deliver you! God bless you.

I'm praying for you!

With love,
Cambria Joy

thank you

I want to thank my first love and King, Jesus Christ, for redeeming one of the most difficult times in my life and working it together for good. This devotional is the physical reminder that He trades our ashes in for beauty.

I also want to thank you, my reader and friend for giving me some space on your bookshelf and in your heart. This is all for you. You are supremely loved.

Thank you to my incredibly brilliant and amazing literary agent, Mike Salisbury, for believing in me and giving me a chance to bring this devotional to life. You have been here every step of the way and words can't express how thankful I am for you and everyone at Yates & Yates.

Thanks to my mom for praying for me and loving for me through my darkest of days. Mom, you are the best of the best.

My editors, Ami McConnell and Karen Yates, you both made my writing come to life in a way I could have never imagined. Thank you both.

Jenn Jett, you are brilliantly creative. It was a privilege to have you design this beautiful devotional, thank you.